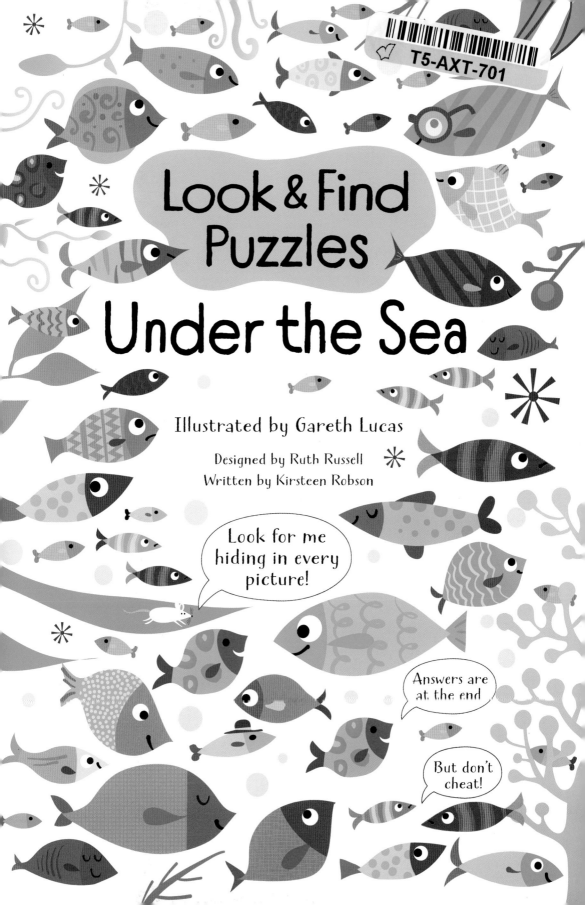

Who's wearing a hat?

2 other spotted fish

2 star earrings like this

3 more purple shells

3

Find three more flying fish like me.

Can you find...

6 more gulls

2 other red oars

4

another one
of these

3 more groups
of bright fish

another
rubber ring

Spot an octopus wearing socks.

6 other starfish

another 2 of these

3 octopuses just like this

Who has a spotted beak?

Can you find...

2 more blue buckets

5 other dominoes

Can you spot a broken pearl necklace?

Where's the key to the treasure chest?

Can you find...

this crab's twin

6 other rings

10

Find a fish with a sparkly tiara on her head.

3 more of these

another golden cup

1 more fish like this

Who's wearing a life jacket?

Can you find... another purple submarine

3 more bananas

12

Find a tiny yellow submarine.

Where did I hang the clothes on the line?

2 other fish like this

another paint brush

2 different cans of paint

13

Can you see a crab riding a dolphin?

Can you find...

a shoe that matches this one

2 more blue bags

14

3 other
carrots

a fish just
like this

another
compass

Spot a fish with a pirate's eye patch.

Can you see a swimming parrot?

Can you find...

3 more pirates' hats

2 other seahorses just like this

Can you find... 3 more goldfish another 3 of these

2 more
toothbrushes

3 blue flags
like this

1 other tube of
toothpaste

Can you find...

2 more
blue shells

a shell that
matches this

Which two seahorses are linking tails?

Spot three little orange fish.

Can you find...   2 more ponies   another jellyfish, just the same

Help me find a yellow fish.

Can you find...

a snow shovel like this

another 3 balls

24

Can you find...

2 more
parrots

another 3
tomatoes

a matching guitar

3 other palm trees

2 fish like this one

Can you find...

1 other
watering can

1 more pink
sunhat

2 bags the same as this

3 more pufferfish

another one of these

Answers

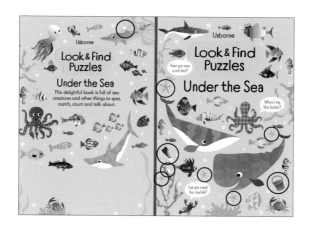

Cover

2–3

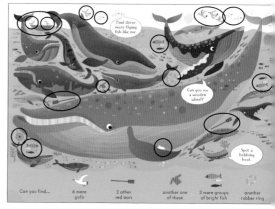

4–5

6–7

8–9

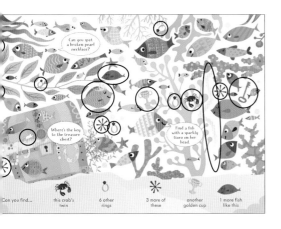

10–11

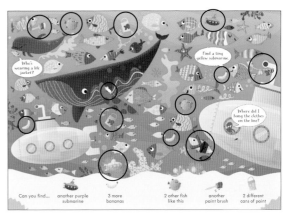

12–13

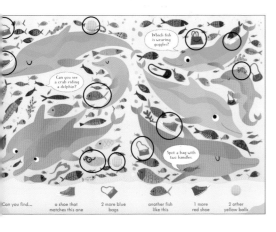

14–15

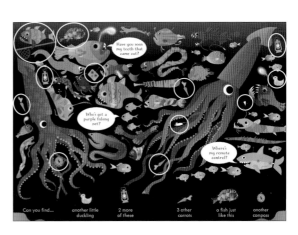

16–17

18–19

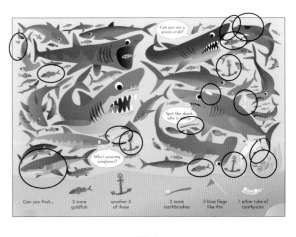

20–21

22–23

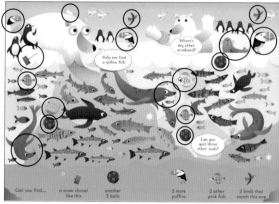

24–25

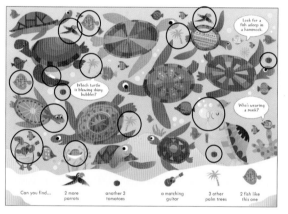

26–27

28–29